The Voyages of
ULYSSES

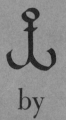

by

Clifton Fadiman

ILLUSTRATED BY WILLIAM M. HUTCHINSON

LEGACY

BOOKS

RANDOM HOUSE New York

J
883
F

12 - 15 - 59

WHAT HAPPENED TO
ULYSSES BEFORE HE STARTED
HIS ADVENTURES

Long, long ago—perhaps three thousand years ago—a great war was fought between the Greeks and the Trojans. Many stories are told of that war and how at last it was won by the Greeks. Partly they won it because of the cunning and wisdom of one of the Greek heroes, the brave Ulysses.

After he and the Greek army conquered Troy, Ulysses ran into bad luck. It took him many years to return to his home on the rocky island of Ithaca where he was king and where his wife Penelope and his son Telemachus had waited for him many long years. During this time strange and wonderful adventures happened to him. The story of some of these adventures is what you are about to read.

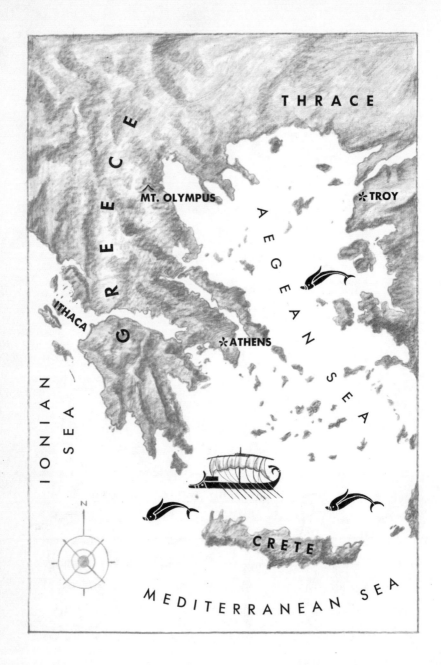

THRACE

GREECE

MT. OLYMPUS

*TROY

ITHACA

AEGEAN SEA

*ATHENS

IONIAN SEA

CRETE

N

MEDITERRANEAN SEA

Ulysses and the Giant Polyphemus

After Ulysses had helped win the war between the Greeks and the Trojans, he and his followers boarded their ships, hoping to reach home quickly. But this was not to be.

For many days Ulysses and his small fleet were tossed about by roaring winds and violent waves. At last, tired and hungry, they approached an island, the land of the Cyclopes.

The Cyclopes were rude, savage giants, with no laws. They lived in stone caves in the mountain tops. They herded their flocks of sheep and goats, each alone, and rarely spoke one to the other. Each was many times the

3

height of a normal man. Each had but one eye in the middle of his forehead.

If they hated the sight of one another, they hated strangers even more. But Ulysses did not know this.

He and his followers landed at night in a thick fog. They killed some of the Cyclopes' goats for food. After they had eaten, they rested the night through. In the morning King Ulysses gathered his men together.

"Friends," he said, "for the time being I want you to stay here. I will go with some of the men of my ship to find out what sort of persons these Cyclopes are, and whether they are friendly to strangers." He picked out the twelve best men in the company. He also took with him beautiful presents to give to the Cyclopes in return for their food and water.

When Ulysses and his men reached the stone cave of one of the Cyclopes, its owner was not at home. They entered the wide, dark mouth of the cave. Inside it was dim and vast. There were baskets of cheeses everywhere, made from goats' milk. There were goats, too, tethered together, filling the cave with their bleatings.

It had taken many hours to find the cave upon the mountaintop. Ulysses and his twelve men were hungry. They killed a fat goat, sacrificed to the gods (for in those days they believed in many gods, not one, as we do today), and roasted it. They ate some of the cheese also, but they took no more than what they could eat in just one meal. Then the Cyclops appeared, huge and terrible. He entered the cave and picked up a stone slab so heavy a hundred ordinary men could not have lifted it. With this he shut the mouth of the cave with as much ease as you close the door to your room. He lit the fire and spied Ulysses and his men sitting there.

"Who are you?" he asked. He had a voice like the deep roar of the wind on a mountaintop.

But the crafty Ulysses did not tell him everything. He spoke of his many adventures and asked for help in the name of Zeus, King of the Gods. But the Cyclops laughed.

"I don't care one bit for Zeus," he said. "I am much stronger than he, and all your other gods." Then he jumped up, seized a couple of Ulysses' brave companions, killed them and ate them. For he loved human flesh.

Then he went to sleep, his snores filling the cave like thunder. The wise Ulysses sat with his remaining men and tried to figure a way out of the dark cave. They could not move the huge boulder. What was he to do?

In the morning the Cyclops awoke. Again he seized two of Ulysses' companions, killed and ate them. Satisfied with his breakfast, he went out, closing the mouth of the cave with the huge rock as he went. All that day in the damp darkness Ulysses and his men sat and thought. But they could not think of a way to get out of their prison.

The wise Ulysses looked about him. Lying close by was a huge trunk of green olive wood which the Cyclops used sometimes as a staff. It was so thick and heavy that it took all of Ulysses' strength and the strength of his men to lift it. They sharpened the staff to a needle point and hardened it in a fire they built. Then they waited.

When the Cyclops returned at night from pasturing his goats, Ulysses offered him a drink of special wine, which he had brought with him as one of the presents for these people, had they turned out to be kind and gracious. The Cyclops drank all the wine. It made him sleepy, and he

They quietly lifted up the sharpened staff

stretched out in his usual resting place beside the fire.

Just before he began to doze off, the wise and crafty Ulysses spoke to him.

"Cyclops," he said, "you wanted to know my name."

"Yes," the Cyclops mumbled, half awake. "Mine is Polyphemus. Tell me yours and I will give you a gift."

"Call me 'Nobody'," cunning Ulysses replied.

"Good," answered Polyphemus. "Here is your gift. Of all your company, I will eat 'Nobody' last."

With a cruel chuckle he fell asleep, snoring.

Then Ulysses and his men quietly lifted up the sharpened staff and with all their might drove it into the eye of

and drove it into the eye of the Cyclops.

the Cyclops, blinding him. He awoke with a terrible scream of pain and rage.

His yells brought other Cyclopes to his door.

"What is the matter, Polyphemus?" they cried out.

"Nobody has blinded me," yelled the Cyclops. "Nobody will kill me."

His friends all laughed at this.

"That's all right," they said. "If *somebody* had done these things, we would lift up the rock and come into your cave to kill him. But since *nobody* has done this to you, we will leave you. Please don't disturb us again with your shouting."

In spite of the Cyclops' cries, off they went.

Now Polyphemus pushed open the rock that guarded the entrance of the cave and sat in the doorway, his arms spread out. He hoped to catch Ulysses and his men as they tried to slip by him. But the cunning Ulysses had thought up another scheme. He went to the biggest sheep he could find and curled himself up under its shaggy belly, holding onto the wool. He ordered his men to do the same with the other sheep.

As the sheep filed out of the cave, the Cyclops could not feel anything except the sheep's wool.

So Ulysses and his companions were able to slip by the blinded monster, into the open air and freedom.

Once aboard their ship Ulysses remembered the deaths

8

The Cyclops could feel nothing except the sheep's wool.

of his companions, and he grew angry. From the bow of
the ship he yelled out to the blinded Polyphemus:

"If anyone asks you how your eye was put out, tell him
that Ulysses blinded you."

9

The monster lifted his blinded eye to heaven and prayed to Poseidon, God of the Sea, to bring disaster to Ulysses and his men. From Olympus, the home of the gods, Poseidon heard him. He grew very angry, for Polyphemus, the Cyclops, was one of his sons. Poseidon swore that he would do his best to make Ulysses' voyage as dangerous as possible. And so it turned out.

"Head for the open sea!" shouted Ulysses. The men bent to their oars, the sails filled, and so they left the dreadful island of the Cyclopes.

Ulysses and the Enchantress Circe

For many days and nights Ulysses and his men sailed over the Mediterranean Sea until they came to the island of Circe. This Circe was a beautiful enchantress.

Ulysses, prudent as always, appointed one of his men to lead a party to Circe's castle. They would ask shelter and food from the enchantress.

As they approached the lonely stone house, they were welcomed by a pack of wolves and lions. These savage beasts were actually victims of Circe's magic and had once been men. For Circe had the power to turn men into beasts.

The lions and wolves greeted Ulysses' scouting party in

friendly fashion, licking and nuzzling them. This strange behavior should have warned Ulysses' men that something was wrong, but they were too weary to take notice. They knocked on Circe's door and she opened it. She invited them to enter.

"Sit down," Circe said. She was a beautiful woman with long black hair and black eyes. She was dressed in a robe of the softest whitest wool. The men thanked her and sat down to eat. The beautiful enchantress gave them food, but into the food she put some of her deadly magic drug. In a twinkling the men were changed to pigs. They had pigs' heads and bristles. They grunted like pigs instead of talking.

The wicked witch drove them into sties she had built for this purpose. She laughed aloud when the poor pigs, whose thoughts were still human, began to cry in their sties.

She flung them some acorns.

"Eat this if you're still hungry," she said. "Cry all you want. No one can hear you."

All the men had been changed into swine except the captain of the scouting band. He had not entered Circe's castle with his men, wisely preferring to wait outside the door. Now, seeing what Circe had done, he ran all the way back to Ulysses' ship and told him what had happened.

Ulysses never hesitated. He knew the duty of a leader. He set out alone to rescue his men from the witch's power.

As Ulysses walked toward Circe's house, a young man approached him and began to talk.

"Where are you off to?" he asked. "I suppose you want to free your men from Circe's clutches. Take care or you may be turned into a pig yourself."

"What can I do?" asked Ulysses. "I must try to save my men."

The young man held out an herb which he had taken from the ground.

"This is the Moly-plant. It will protect you against the power of the witch's spell."

As the young man handed the wise Ulysses the magic herb, he smiled. Ulysses knew then that this was no mortal man but the mighty Hermes, God of Travelers. The god smiled once more and sprang away toward the mighty mountain of Olympus where the gods all dwelt.

Meanwhile Ulysses was knocking at Circe's door. She let him in and gave him food into which she had mixed her drug. But the holy plant Hermes had given him protected Ulysses from the drug's effects. He drank and ate the poisoned food and wine safely. Circe's black magic could not prevail against Ulysses' god-given strength. The enchantress was so amazed at the man who could resist her witchcraft that she was ready to do anything for him.

When he asked Circe to return his men to him in their original shape, she did as she was bid. Soon the great hall of the castle rang with shouts of joy as the enchantress' magic oil was rubbed on the pigs and they returned one by one to human shape.

Now neither Ulysses nor his band had anything to fear from the enchantress. So for a month they stayed with Circe, eating, drinking, resting their tired bodies.

After a month had passed, Circe noticed how restless Ulysses was becoming. She took him aside one night and spoke to him, as his men laughed and drank and listened to music in her banquet hall.

"Wise Ulysses," Circe said, "if you wish to see again your own castle in Ithaca, I can tell you what you must do."

When she said this, tears came to Ulysses' eyes. He thought of his wife Penelope and his young son Telemachus, whom he had left as a baby many years before when he had gone off to fight in the war against Troy.

Then Circe said, "Your next adventure will be with the Sirens, who bewitch everyone who approaches them. You must be careful of their lovely singing. If you fall under their spell, they will make sure that you never get home. You will recognize them as you sail past their land, for they sit in a meadow piled high with the bones of the unfortunate men they have bewitched in the past. You must

14

Circe returned the men to their original shape.

plug the ears of your men with wax so that they cannot hear the fatal Sirens' song. If you wish to listen, you must make your men strap you to the mast, hand and foot. Then you will be able to listen to the Sirens without danger."

Ulysses thanked Circe for her warning. He began to get up, but she held him back.

"There are other dangers," she said. "Once past the Sirens, you will have to sail past Scylla and Charybdis. You will see two rocks rising out of the sea. One is the home of the monster Scylla. She has a bark like a puppy, but she is terrible nonetheless. She has twelve feet, all dangling in air, and six long necks each with its own head. Each head has a triple row of teeth. She fishes for men, and no crew can say they have ever passed by the monster without losing at least six of their company.

"The other of the two rocks, near Scylla's rock, is the home of the dreadful Charybdis. If you get near her, she will destroy you utterly, for her work is to suck down the dark water and vomit it up again. Once your ship is caught in this whirlpool, nothing on earth can save you, not even the gods. So you must hug the side of Scylla's rock, and make up your mind to lose six of your brave friends, rather than go down with your ship into Charybdis' whirlpool and all be destroyed.

"Your next port will be the island of Thrinacia, where the Sun God Apollo has his herd of cattle. These are not

The ship scudded over the waves—away from Circe's island.

ordinary cattle; they are half divine. Goddesses shepherd them. This is my warning: Do not touch them in any way, and you may then get safely home. But if you touch them, more trouble will come upon you."

Circe finished her warnings as the sun rose over the horizon. Ulysses and his men thanked her. They climbed into their swift black ship. A good wind filled their sails, and they scudded over the waves.

The Sirens—
Scylla and Charybdis—
the Sacred Cattle

As the Greeks approached the island of the Sirens, Ulysses ordered his men to plug their ears with wax. Ulysses had himself strapped to the mast. Then he heard the Sirens' song. It was so beautiful that if he had not been tied he would have dived into the waters and swum to them. He strained at the straps with all of his strength, but, obeying Ulysses' orders, his men refused to untie him. And so they rowed on until the song had faded into the distance, and then Ulysses was released. Their first danger was past.

Now they were approaching the narrow passage between the two black rocks. Remembering Circe's warning, Ulysses

Hearing the Sirens' song, Ulysses strained at the straps.

hugged the side of Scylla's rock and avoided the roaring whirlpool of Charybdis. But, just as Circe had foretold, six men were snatched from the ship by the six heads of the monster Scylla. As Ulysses sailed by, he heard their screams as they were eaten. Tears ran down his face. Still it was better to lose six than to lose all.

19

So they neared the island of Apollo the Sun God. Here Apollo kept his herds of sacred sheep and cattle. The wise Ulysses wished to continue the journey without stopping, for Circe had warned him of the island. His men, however, were tired and unhappy after the horrors they had lived through. Against Ulysses' warnings, they beached the ship on the island. Ulysses made them all promise not to touch any of the god's cattle.

This was fine as long as the food and drink Circe had given them lasted. But a storm came out of the west and continued for a whole month. They could not sail on the violent sea. Little by little the food, wine and water were all eaten up.

The men grew hungry and bad tempered. They waited until a morning when Ulysses was asleep. While he was unaware of what they were doing, they killed the forbidden cattle and roasted the flesh.

When Ulysses awoke and smelled the odor of roasting meat, he knew his men had disobeyed him, and that the gods would be very angry.

From the heights of Mount Olympus, Apollo heard the cries of his cattle as they were killed for meat. He rushed to Zeus, the King of the Gods, and demanded that the men be punished for what they had done. Zeus listened to his demand and agreed to it.

Ulysses, knowing that the damage had now been done,

While Ulysses slept, they killed the forbidden cattle.

allowed his crew to finish what they had started. So for six days they feasted on Apollo's cattle. On the seventh day the storm died down and the sun shone. Ulysses and his band of brave but foolish men went aboard the black ship, and they pulled away from the island.

Zeus, remembering his promise to Apollo, hurled a lightning bolt that smashed the ship to pieces. The black ship sank beneath the waves, and all the crew were drowned. Only the wily Ulysses survived. He managed to cling to a piece of wood that was floating on the water. For nine days and nights he drifted until the wood washed him up on the island of Ogygia, home of the nymph Calypso.

21

Ulysses and Calypso

For seven years Ulysses stayed a prisoner of the beautiful nymph Calypso. She loved him very much and, though he begged her, she would not let him continue the journey toward his home where his faithful wife Penelope and his son Telemachus had almost given up hope that he was still alive. He lived with Calypso in her cave. During the day he would go to the shore of the island and look in the direction of Ithaca, and weep for his homeland.

It is possible that things might have gone on in this fashion until Ulysses' death, for he had no boat and no crew to help him sail it even if he had had one. However, at the end of seven years, Zeus changed his mind and decided to help Ulysses. This is how it happened:

In those times gods and goddesses had favorites among the mortal men and women. The goddess Athene was very fond of Ulysses. For seven years she watched Ulysses' sadness on Calypso's island. Finally she went to Zeus and begged him to release Ulysses. Zeus listened to her. He sent Hermes, the messenger of the gods, to the far island where Calypso held Ulysses captive. There Hermes told the nymph of Zeus's decision. Since all gods and goddesses had to obey their King, Calypso promised to let Ulysses go.

The beautiful nymph put down her weaving and walked to the shore of the island, where Ulysses spent his days looking toward Ithaca, his eyes streaming with tears.

"Ulysses," she said, "there is no more need for you to spend your life on this island. I am willing to help you leave it. But you must make your own boat from the trees. I will put in it bread and wine so that you may keep alive on your journey."

Ulysses jumped to his feet and thanked her with all his heart, hoping that at last his troubles were over and that he would see his wife and his son again.

He went to the forest and cut down trees. Then with simple tools he made himself a boat so small that he could sail it alone. It took the wise Ulysses only four days. He was a cunning shipwright and, besides, he wanted badly to get home.

On the morning of the fifth day beautiful Calypso saw him off. His boat was loaded with food. She called up a breeze to fill his sails. With happy heart Ulysses sailed away from the island where he had spent seven long years. With tears in her eyes Calypso watched him go, for she loved him and had wished to make him immortal. But she knew that he was destined at last to reach his wife Penelope and his son Telemachus.

Yet Ulysses' troubles were not ended. For Poseidon, God of the Sea, was still furious at the blinding of his son Polyphemus. He spied the hero in his home-built boat and frowned in anger. Now Poseidon raised ocean waves the height of a house. The sky turned black. Ulysses saw the storm coming and held on as hard as he could.

An enormous wave bore down on him. It scattered the boat on the surface of the sea, ripping loose the leather bindings.

Bruised and battered by the waves, Ulysses found a piece of timber and hung on for dear life. He would have drowned if the sea nymph Ino had not risen beside him and said to him:

"Wise Ulysses, why do the gods make your way so difficult? Take this veil and put it around your middle. It is magic and will protect you against any injury or death.

Now Poseidon raised ocean waves the height of a house.

Then cast off from your piece of timber and swim toward
land."

Grateful for this help, Ulysses put on the nymph's gift
and began to swim. He was a strong man, one of the
strongest of the Greek heroes. For two days and two nights
he wrestled with the boiling seas. On the morning of the

third day he was completely tired out. But ahead of him was the country of the Phaeacians.

He stumbled onto the beach. Near him a river wandered into the forest. He followed it up the beach and into the forest itself. There, by the side of the river, he made himself a bed, digging it out with his hands.

Ulysses Reaches Home

The king of the Phaeacians was called Alcinoüs. His country was rich, and the land grew much food. He had a lovely daughter named Nausicaä.

As the night turned to morning, wise Ulysses lay sleeping near the stream he had found. He was tired after his long swim. His broad chest rose and fell as he slept, and the leaves that covered it fluttered down with a rustling sound.

That morning the young princess came to the stream to wash her clothes. As she dipped them in the river, with her friends all around her, she saw Ulysses sleeping in

The Princess gave a shriek, and the hero awoke.

the shade. She gave a shriek, and the hero awoke. From
the noble look of the princess, he realized that she must
be a king's daughter. He threw himself on her mercy and
begged her for aid and shelter.

His voice was so gentle, in spite of his size and his
bulging muscles, that the Princess Nausicaä called to her
friends who were running away as fast as they could and
told them to return. Nausicaä had never seen such a man

as Ulysses. She liked him right away, and hoped that he would stay awhile with her so that she might get to know him better.

She gave Ulysses food and told him how to find the palace of her father King Alcinoüs.

The palace was large and beautiful. The King welcomed Ulysses with kindness and put before him a bowl of mellow wine. Then he asked him to tell of his adventures. Ulysses talked far into the night. He told about the giant Polyphemus and the Sirens and Scylla and Charybdis and all the other perils that he had overcome, until at last he had been cast up on Alcinoüs' shores. His audience was spellbound. The Phaeacians made no sound, not even a whisper, as they listened for hours.

Then the King asked Ulysses who he was. Until then Ulysses had not given Alcinoüs his name, but now he told him.

The next day King Alcinoüs gave Ulysses many royal gifts and put a boat at his disposal. The strongest and bravest of the King's young men were the rowers.

After Ulysses had boarded the boat, he fell fast asleep. The royal gifts King Alcinoüs had given him were by his side. The young men rowed swiftly, and a good wind filled the sails. Athene, Ulysses' guardian goddess, protected the hero and sped him on his way.

All day and all night the young men rowed, and the

ship sailed on. In the early morning they reached Ithaca, the land where Ulysses was king, the dear, rocky island he had not seen for almost twenty years. They drove the black ship upon the beach and put Ulysses, still sleeping, on the sand, with his gifts beside him. Then, their work done, they sailed back to their own country.

The wise Ulysses slept on, not knowing that he had finally reached home, not knowing the terrible thing he would still have to do before he could be king once more in Ithaca.

Ulysses Meets the Suitors

When he awoke later in the morning, he did not know where he was. Everything had changed in the long time he had been away. He thought he was in some strange land. He clenched his fists and cried out against the cruel fate that had once again cheated him.

In the middle of the crying and wailing, the Goddess Athene appeared to him in the shape of a tall, beautiful woman. But Ulysses knew her immediately.

"Do not cry out," the Goddess told him smiling. "You are truly back in Ithaca, your home."

Ulysses did not believe her at first, but she convinced

31

For years Penelope wove each day at a beautiful rug,

him. He was so happy he kissed the ground at the Goddess' feet.

Then the wise Ulysses hid his treasure in a nearby cave. The Goddess said to him:

"You must not be recognized. For three years a gang of young men have been eating your faithful wife, Penelope, out of house and home. They all say that you are dead. They have asked your wife to choose a second husband from among them. But patient Penelope cannot believe that you will not return. Cunningly she has delayed her decision. For years she wove a beautiful rug during the day, telling the suitors that she could not make up her mind among them until the work was finished. But at

while the suitors waited for her to make up her mind.

night, secretly, she undid her day's work. But no matter
how she delayed her marriage, the suitors continued to
live in the courtyard of your house. They eat all their
meals in your eating hall; they feast far into the night.
You can imagine how they are using up your food and
your cattle, for there are one hundred and eight of them.
All are strong young noblemen from Ithaca and the islands
and mainland near by."

Hearing this story, Ulysses' heart grew hard within him.
He knew that he must punish these evil suitors for the
hand of Penelope. But what could he, a single man, do
against so many?

As the Goddess spoke, she changed Ulysses into a

ragged old man. Then she cheered up the hero and told him to be of good heart. She said that the first person he must find in order to begin his revenge upon the suitors was the old swineherd who tended Ulysses' herds of pigs. He was loyal and had never believed for a minute that his master was dead.

Ulysses thanked the mighty Goddess, and followed a rough track leading into the woods and through the hills toward the hut of the old swineherd, whose name was Eumaeus.

He found him sitting in front of his hut. The old man did not recognize the ragged figure approaching him. Ulysses told him that he was a lonely beggar, hoping to find something to eat and drink at the house of the King of Ithaca. The generous-hearted herdsman took pity on him and invited him in for a meal.

Once Ulysses had eaten and drunk, he let the old swineherd tell him all the gossip. He learned many things. He found out that his son, Telemachus, now a young man of twenty, had sailed away on a ship to try to find his father. For Telemachus had never believed in Ulysses' death. He had hoped to find his father and bring him back to teach the evil suitors a lesson, for he alone was too young and inexperienced to protect his mother and his household from their arrogance.

Ulysses found out that the suitors had tried to murder

Telemachus, and that they had failed. His son had escaped death, but Eumaeus did not know where he was.

Though the old man did not know he was speaking to his master, his loyalty and love made Ulysses very happy. He felt that he had one friend he could rely on. However, wise Ulysses still did not tell the swineherd who he really was.

That night Ulysses slept in Eumaeus' hut. In the morning they had breakfast together. The old swineherd sighed as he finished his meal.

"If only my master were back from the Trojan wars," he said, "he'd make quick work of those suitors."

"He is nearer than you think," Ulysses replied. "I even believe he is very near to Ithaca."

"You'll never get me to believe that," Eumaeus said.

Then the swineherd went to his day's work.

Meanwhile the Goddess Athene had appeared before Telemachus and had bidden him return to his home. The young man was staying with friends on another island until he felt it safe to return to his palace, filled with the murderous suitors.

As quickly as he could, Telemachus obeyed the Goddess. He did not know that he would find his father upon his return. Yet he was still convinced that King Ulysses was alive.

Landing in Ithaca, the young Telemachus went instantly

to the hut of the swineherd Eumaeus, knowing that Eumaeus was one of the few servants who had remained completely loyal to his absent King.

When he arrived, Eumaeus jumped up in amazement and kissed Telemachus on both cheeks.

"You are back," he said, tears running down his face. "I thought I should never see you again."

Ulysses rose, too, his heart moved at the sight of his tall son, who had been a mere baby when Ulysses had left for the war. Telemachus, of course, did not recognize his father in this ragged beggar. However, he politely insisted that Ulysses sit down, and the wise King did so. How he longed to hug his long-lost son and kiss him! But he said nothing, for he was far-sighted and knew that things must not be hurried.

Then Telemachus asked for news of his mother, the faithful Penelope. Eumaeus told him that she had not yet made up her mind. The suitors were still in the banquet hall, eating her food, drinking her wine, boasting, quarreling among themselves for the hand of Penelope.

"Even the pigs I guard for your great father are fewer in number," the old swineherd said. "I can't keep up with those hundred and eight greedy mouths. They are eating and drinking up all your possessions."

"Go secretly to my mother," Telemachus said. "Tell her that I am home safe. Our house is full of my enemies, and

The old swineherd jumped up in amazement.

I don't think it would be wise for me to show myself there right away."

The faithful old swineherd trudged off to do his errand, and Ulysses and his son were left alone together. At that moment the Goddess Athene appeared to Ulysses, invisible to everyone but him. She motioned him out of the hut and spoke softly to him.

"Now is the time to let your son know who you are, so that the two of you may plot your revenge against the suitors." As she spoke, Athene touched Ulysses with her magic golden wand, and he became again as he had been. His face filled out, the tan returned to his cheeks, he grew tall and strong, every inch of him King Ulysses. He was now dressed in splendid clothes. Ulysses returned to the hut.

Telemachus could not believe his eyes.

"Are you a god?" he asked. "You are not the same man who was here a moment ago."

"I am your father," Ulysses said, and a tear coursed down his cheek. "I am Ulysses, returned to my kingdom."

"I don't believe you," Telemachus replied.

"It is so," Ulysses said. "The gods are on my side. This change in me is the work of Athene. She changed my appearance for a while, but now I am here in my true form."

Telemachus, at last convinced, took his father in his

arms, crying with joy. After a while they sat down. There was no time to lose. They began to plan their campaign against the suitors who had invaded King Ulysses' palace.

In the morning Telemachus went to his father's castle, leaving Ulysses behind. Once there, he comforted his mother, the patient Penelope, and told her that somehow he felt sure that Ulysses was still alive. But he said nothing of the fact that his father was in Eumaeus' hut, waiting, plotting his revenge. The time had not yet come for that.

Meanwhile Ulysses again took on the shape of an old beggar. He then went toward his palace as a stranger. In his magic disguise he was not recognized by anyone. He entered the huge banquet hall, where the suitors were eating, drinking and insulting his servants and his son. The air was thick with the odor of wine and the smell of roasting meat. Ulysses entered his own house humbly, like the beggar he seemed to be.

Just as he came to the threshold, an old dog lying in a pile of refuse raised his head. His name was Argus. He had been Ulysses' favorite pet. Now no one gave him enough to eat, and he was at the point of death. He wagged his tail feebly and dropped his ears, though he had not enough strength to come to his master. Ulysses brushed away a tear at the sight of his faithful hound, so neglected and abused. The dog Argus, having recognized Ulysses, dropped his head on his paws and died happy. He alone,

of all in Ulysses' palace, had not been fooled by the magic disguise.

Ulysses entered the crowded banquet hall and sat down. Telemachus recognized him at once since this was all part of their plan. He sent him a basket of food to eat.

Then Antinoüs, the leader of the gang of suitors, looked rudely at Ulysses.

"Haven't we got enough beggars as it is?" Antinoüs asked Telemachus. "There's hardly enough food for us, let alone every old man who wishes a free meal."

But Telemachus reminded him of the laws of hospitality.

Then Ulysses, to test him, asked for more food. Antinoüs grew so angry at this that the prudent Ulysses held his tongue, waiting until his time should come.

Disguised as a beggar, Ulysses entered his own house.

At this point there entered into the banquet hall a real beggar, a good-for-nothing fellow named Irus.

He went at once to where Ulysses was sitting, for he felt that another beggar in the hall would take food and wine away from him.

"You'd better leave," he said rudely to Ulysses. "This is my spot you're in. You're not wanted here."

"Be careful," replied Ulysses, really angry. "Or you may be sorry you talked to me in this way."

"Sorry indeed!" Irus said, feeling that he himself was far stronger than this feeble old beggar. "If you want to fight, I'm ready anytime."

The cruel Antinoüs laughed loudly.

"I have an idea," he said. "Let the two beggars fight it out. The one who wins shall have this delicious roast meat that I had set aside for my supper. He shall be called King of the Beggars, and we will allow no one else to beg in this place."

Antinoüs said this because he wished Irus to give the old beggar a terrible beating.

Then Ulysses rose and threw aside his beggar's rags, showing his strong muscles and his big chest. Irus was much afraid, but the suitors' servants forced him to face the strange old man.

Ulysses wondered whether to kill him with one blow, but decided it would be better just to knock him out. Irus, forced to fight, hit Ulysses once on the shoulder. Then Ulysses hit him in the jaw so hard that Irus fell down on the floor, bleeding and unconscious. The suitors grew silent, for the fight had not gone as they had expected. Ulysses dragged Irus out by the foot and returned to claim his reward.

The suitors grew angry at Ulysses. Everyone began to shout. Telemachus rose to his feet and stopped the noise.

"I think you should all go home," he said. "Now that

42

you have eaten and drunk there is no need to linger here."

The suitors listened to his words. They rose from the tables, and went their ways to their own homes. They knew that they would be there again soon, eating Ulysses' food, drinking his wine, and courting his faithful wife.

King Ulysses was left alone in the empty banquet hall to plan his revenge.

King Ulysses was left alone to plan his revenge.

The Revenge of
Ulysses

Ulysses completed his plan and spoke to his son Telemachus.

"The swords must be put away," he told him. "All the weapons hanging on the walls in the house must be hidden. The suitors will then have nothing to defend themselves with. That is the only way that the two of us can win against a hundred and eight men."

Telemachus took down all the weapons and put them away in Ulysses' storehouse.

After this Telemachus went to his bed. Penelope asked that the beggar man be brought to her so that she might ask him news of her husband. She did this with every stranger, always hoping to hear of Ulysses.

Ulysses let her talk. Then he told her that he had met Ulysses in Crete, and that he felt the King would soon be home.

Penelope could not believe him.

"Let me test you," she said. "Tell me what Ulysses looked like when you knew him at your place in Crete." For the wily Ulysses had told Penelope a lot of untruths, knowing it was not yet time to reveal himself in his true form.

Then Ulysses described Penelope's husband. He mentioned a number of things, including the name of a servant that Ulysses had had with him. Penelope was convinced then that the old beggar man had really known her husband, and her sad heart was filled with hope.

"You will be an honored guest in this house," she said. She called her old nurse, Eurycleia, to wash her guest's feet.

When the nurse had set out a basin of water, she took off Ulysses' sandals and began to clean his feet. In a moment she recognized an old hunting scar that Ulysses had received many years before. Then she knew who the beggar man really was. She was about to cry out in joy and wonder, but Ulysses clapped his hand to her mouth and swore her to secrecy.

"I have decided on a test of strength and skill."

The next day, as the suitors were eating and drinking, Penelope appeared before them. In her hand she held Ulysses' own bow, so thick and strong that only a man of enormous strength could use it. With her she had a box full of axes. She raised her white arm, and the suitors all stopped eating.

"My lords," she said, "I have made up my mind at last. You have eaten up my wise husband's food and have drunk his drink too long. I have decided on a test of strength and skill. Whichever man among you can string this great bow which belonged to my husband, and shoot an arrow

46

through every one of the twelve ax handles, as my husband did, that man will I marry."

The night before, Penelope had mentioned her plan to the old beggar, not knowing he was her husband. Ulysses had approved of it since it fitted in with his own plans for revenge. He had persuaded Penelope to follow through with her test.

Telemachus then dug a single, long, shallow trench for the axes. He planted them in the beaten earth of the banquet hall, in a row, one behind the other. Then he stepped away and tried to string Ulysses' bow. Three times he tried, and he would have succeeded on the fourth attempt had not his father in beggar's disguise shaken his head at him. So Telemachus admitted he could not handle the bow of Ulysses.

All the suitors then began to try to string the bow. A half dozen had tried without success, when Ulysses rose.

"Gentlemen," he said, "I wonder whether you would let *me* have a try. I would like to see what strength there is left in my feeble body."

The suitors were very much against this, for they were afraid the strange beggar, who had proved himself so strong in the fight with Irus, would be able to succeed where they had failed. But Telemachus put them into a good humor.

"After all," he said, "a common beggar can't beat us.

After testing the bow to make sure it had not cracked,

But surely it would be amusing to see the old man try."

The proud suitors laughed this time. Ulysses picked up his bow and went to the threshold of the banquet hall. At the same time the loyal swineherd Eumaeus called the nurse Eurycleia to his side. Ulysses had told him who he was the night before, and the loyal swineherd had sworn to keep the secret and to help Ulysses.

"Eurycleia," Eumaeus said, "leave the banquet hall. Lock the door behind you. Go to the room where the women are and lock them in. No matter what cries or

he took one arrow, drew the bowstring back and shot.

shouts you may hear, keep them away from this hall."

Eurycleia did as the loyal swineherd told her.

Then Ulysses took his bow in his hands. He tested it to make sure it had not cracked in the many years it had been unused. Then he strung it as easily as if it had been a child's toy. He took one arrow and, without seeming to aim, drew the bowstring back and shot. Through the ax handles the arrow flew, missing none in its flight. Then, as the suitors' faces turned white with fear, the mighty Ulysses leaped to the entrance door of the hall and poured out at his feet the great quiver of long, deadly arrows.

"Now for another target," he shouted. Straight at Antinoüs he leveled an arrow.

The suitor was about to drink when Ulysses' arrow pierced his throat. He fell dead to the floor. The suitors roared in anger and looked for weapons on the wall. But the cunning Ulysses had taken them all away the night before, and the hundred and eight were defenseless against the one.

"You dogs," Ulysses shouted. "You never thought you'd see me back from Troy. Here I am, and each one of you will die for your greed and your disloyalty to your King."

Then Ulysses began to shoot, picking off the suitors one by one as they rushed at him. It was dreadful to see. The floor swam with blood. The bodies of the suitors were piled up, one upon the other like a catch of fish. While he was shooting, Ulysses sent Telemachus to his storehouse to bring him a sword and shield. Telemachus returned with the weapons as Ulysses' last arrow was loosed. Then the mighty King and his noble son Telemachus fought with their swords. For a while the suitors tried to stand against, Ulysses and Telemachus. But the Goddess Athene was on the side of the King of Ithaca, and she made every try of the suitors come to nothing. Finally the hall was filled with the groans of dying men. The last suitor had been killed, and Ulysses was victorious.

Then the mighty king and his son fought with their swords.

Ulysses called the old nurse to him, and she and the women servants cleaned up the hall and made it smell sweet again. The bodies were taken outside. Ulysses stood, leaning upon his sword, looking at the home he had never thought to see again.

The old nurse hurried to Penelope's room, crying,

"Wake up, Penelope. Your own husband Ulysses is home. Come and see."

But Penelope did not believe her.

"All the suitors are dead," the old nurse told her, "and Ulysses waits for you in his banquet hall."

At this Penelope rose and went to where Ulysses was sitting, waiting for her. She did not know what to do, whether to put her arms around this ragged man or to question him. She was still not sure who he was.

The wise Ulysses understood.

"I will wait," he said, "until I have bathed and I have put on clean clothes. Then you can test me, and you will see that I am truly your husband."

He bathed himself and put on clean clothes. The Goddess Athene did her part, too. She gave Ulysses back his youth and his good looks. Then he went to Penelope.

"Surely," Ulysses said, "you recognize me now, my dear wife."

But the wise Penelope, still wishing to test this handsome stranger, turned to the old nurse. "Come, Eurycleia, make him up a comfortable bed outside the bedroom. Take the big bed from inside and make it up."

Ulysses frowned.

"It is impossible to move that bed," he said. "The bedpost is not only a bedpost, as you well know, but the trunk of a huge olive tree which has helped to hold up our house. This has always been a secret between us."

Then Penelope, at last, knew him for her husband. She threw herself weeping into his arms, and the two were together for the first time in almost twenty years!

King Ulysses had at last come home.

Legacy Books